D0574281
Hugs,
Rocky Bear

Written, Photographed, and
Designed By Candy Bridgman

For Jack -
Enjoy,
Candy Bridgman

ROCKY Bear Publishing
www.aspenbearpub.com

To Rocky Nelson and Carol Hooper

Thank you for providing your exquisite
bear photos... pg. 20 and pg. 28

First edition, Printed in China
ISBN: 978-0-615-24488-4

Summary: ROCKY Bear wants to live on Aspen
Mountain, but heads to the town of Aspen for pizza and
other goodies as the food supply on the mountain
becomes difficult to find.

ROCKY Bear Publishing
1327 Vine Street
Aspen, CO 81611
www.aspenbearpub.com

On the edge of the Roaring Fork River in Aspen, Colorado, roams a black bear named ROCKY.

Every autumn ROCKY hikes the river looking for
the last bite of food before her long winter's nap

ROCKY spent the past summer hanging out among the Aspen trees eating grasses and flowering plants. When a change of weather dries the grass, ROCKY turns to berries (serviceberry, thimbleberry, twinberry and chokecherry) for her meals. She likes to snack on ants and insects.

ROCKY spends most of her day looking for food. She eats 40 pounds of berries and nuts in one day. This large amount of food helps her gain a few pounds each day to store enough fuel for the winter.

The mountain side turns a golden color as seasons change. This is ROCKY's sign to search the thick forest for a place to make her den. She will return before the ground freezes to dig her bed of leaves, bark and wood chips.

After selecting her winter bed, she sees a group of BIGHORN sheep playing in the forest. But ROCKY doesn't stay to play as she is in a hurry to search for a tasty snack.

ROCKY comes to a ridge with a view of the town of Aspen. The thought of good tasting pizza is on her mind. She waits until early morning to seek out her favorite dish.

ROCKY wanders into a home with a screen door left open.

The scent of last night's dinner leads her to the kitchen. While standing on her hind legs to reach the cabinet, the pantry tumbles down. Food spills everywhere. ROCKY enjoys a feast of pizza, muffins, cookies, honey and fresh blueberry pie.

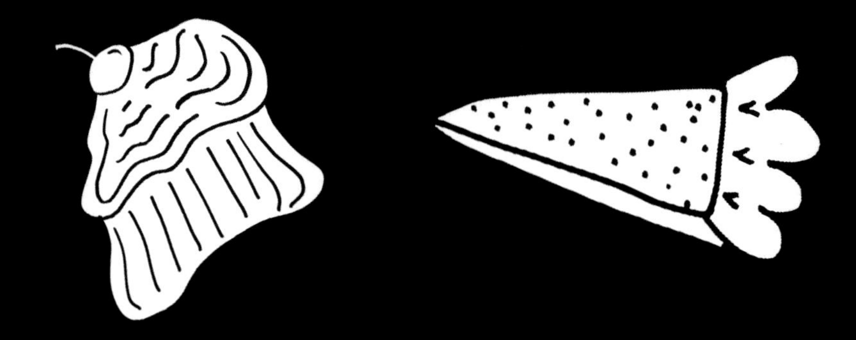

The homeowner awakens to a loud noise and calls the police. Alarms are sounded!

ROCKY is frightened and runs out the door leaving a trail of goodies. She finds a cozy spot under the deck to lick her sticky paws.

HONEY

BEAR DAILY NEWS

a.m. break-in ...ROCKY Bear trapped in a wire cage

Officer Rob arrives at the home explaining to the homeowner: "People don't understand that feeding the bears will teach them to come back for the tasty and plentiful human food." The homeowner realizes this actually puts the bear in danger when Officer Rob explains: "Once a bear is trapped, it is removed and relocated 50 miles away. If the bear gets into trouble a second time, it will not be able to live in Aspen again." The officer gives ROCKY a red tag that states she is a "Nuisance Bear" and carts her far, far away.

ROCKY doesn't want to be known as a "Nuisance Bear," but she misses her home. She starts her journey back to her beloved mountain.

Travelling over hills and valleys, she views the Maroon Bells, a well-known mountain formation. She hears bells ringing, and senses she is close to Aspen Mountain.

Photo by Rocky Nelson

On her trip, she thinks of luscious fruit waiting for her. ROCKY is very tired when she gets to Aspen. She knows it is risky to eat in town, but she is hungry.

She rests in a tree enjoying her favorite tiny red crab apples. ROCKY goes to her winter den when she no longer finds food to eat.

Sleeping is ROCKY's way to survive the cold, long winter months without food. Her cave is deep under tree roots, but she has been known to hibernate in hollow trees, mine shafts and under rocks.

While ROCKY hibernates, her heart beats slowly. Her body uses food stored to give her energy while she sleeps.

She dreams of waking to fields of flowers, grasses and berries on the mountain.

Often, ROCKY wakes early to find skiers and snowboarders on the mountain. She strolls back to her den to sleep until spring.

When spring arrives, ROCKY awakens to the smell of fresh grass. "Yum," she mumbles as she eats her first meal. She is hungry after a six month snooze.

Photo by Carol Hooper

ROCKY hugs the trunk of an aspen tree for a good morning stretch.

Humming is ROCKY's way to announce to the world, she loves living on Aspen Mountain.

Find out how you can help her stay there.

What is wrong with this picture?

ROCKY wants to stay on Aspen Mountain. These are simple ways to help ROCKY and her bear friends stay out of trouble.

1. Use a bear-proof garbage container

2. Remove bird feeders from April to November

3. Lock all doors/windows (including vehicles)

4. Keep barbeque grills clean

5. Keep vehicles free of food and beverage

6. Avoid planting fruit, nut or berry trees

Thank you for not feeding ROCKY. You are helping ROCKY eat a healthy bear diet, and live in the woods on Aspen Mountain.

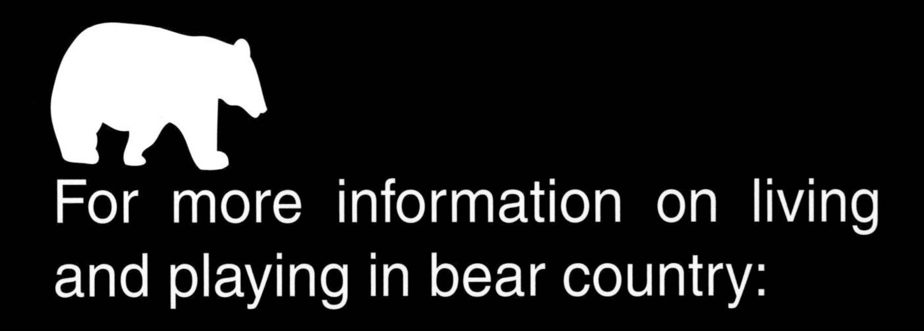

For more information on living and playing in bear country:

www.aspenbearpub.com

www. aspenbears.com

www.bearsmart.com

www.roaringforkbears.com

www.wildearthguardians.org

www.wildlife.state.co.us

A BEARY SPECIAL THANKS

To my sons: *Andy, Steve and Scotty Bridgman*
Thanks for supporting my passion for bears,
and my first book ever. I love you.

To my friends: *Bill Bridgman, Ellen Goldenberg, Carol Hooper, Dusty Nusbaum, Jean Patterson*
Thank you for your knowledge and support
in making Aspen's ROCKY Bear a great read
for children and adults.

And to the following:

Kevin Wright, ***Colorado Division of Wildlife,*** for providing accurate information about bear life in the Rockies.

Mike Bartholomew, ***Overseas Printing*** - *San Francisco,*
and Marcelo Rossetti, **Rossetti Design International,** for bringing a gold standard to the production and design of this book.

Gabriela & Alejandro Rossetti (ages 6 & 3) for bringing a child's perspective to the book.